Matthew Syed

5

YOU ARE AWESOME

WORKBOOKS

TIMES TABLES

MADE EASY

wren
& rook

NOTES TO PARENTS, CARERS AND KIDS!

*Hi there! It's me, Matthew Syed. I wanted to let you know that getting good at stuff is not
as hard as it seems. In fact, anyone can get better at almost anything. With practice, hard
work and a positive mindset YOU can become BRILLIANT at times tables! So come on,
let's get started and first of all get into a growth mindset groove by saying out loud:
"With practice and determination I can become AWESOME at times tables!"*

- *Sit down in a quiet place, where you won't be distracted by little brothers or sisters.*

- *Read through the instructions together and discuss any difficult words.*

- *Have some spare pieces of paper ready for working out tougher calculations.*

- *Use a pencil so that mistakes can be rubbed out before trying again!*

- *Read through the instructions together and discuss anything you might find difficult.*

- *Try to find out why mistakes were made and what to do to get the right answer.*

- *Remember: Practice Makes ~~Perfect~~ Awesome!*

Let's find our maths mojo and dive in!

Matthew Syed

MY "GETTING GOOD AT TABLES" PROGRESS CHART

Tick each section off as you complete it.

THE 2 TIMES TABLE

The 2 times table involves doubling, or adding two of the same number together to get the answer. So if I have 3 cars and my brother has 3 cars, that equals 6 cars and this is written as:

You are already awesome at so many things ... annoying your kid brother (me too), demolishing a strawberry ice cream (also me), so get ready to find your confidence at the 2 times table!

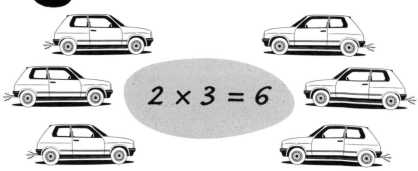

$$2 \times 3 = 6$$

TIMES TABLE TIME!

$2 \times 3 =$

$2 \times 6 =$

$2 \times 9 =$

$2 \times 1 =$

$2 \times 4 =$

$2 \times 8 =$

$2 \times 2 =$

$2 \times 10 =$

$2 \times 12 =$

$2 \times 5 =$

$2 \times 11 =$

So, how did you do?

If you didn't get them all right, have another go! With practice, you'll smash it.

Times tables tips

Because 2 is an even number, all the answers to the 2 times table are even numbers.

4

PAIRS

Two of any number is called a pair.

How many pairs of my trainers (sorry for the pong!) can you see here?

How many trainers are there in 6 pairs?

How many fingers are there on a pair of gloves?

MIND-BLOWING MULTIPLES

A multiple is a number that is made by multiplying one number by another.

Circle all of the numbers below that **aren't** multiples of 2.

4 8 7 12 10 9 17 18

HALVES

You can also use the 2 times table to find half of something.

My brother and I are about to play a table tennis match. We have 12 ping pong balls and we want to divide them so that we both have the same amount. How many do we each have?

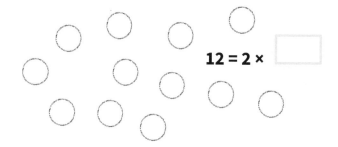

12 = 2 ×

Your mum has been to the bakery. She bought 10 croissants and has promised to give you and your friend half each. How many croissants will you get?

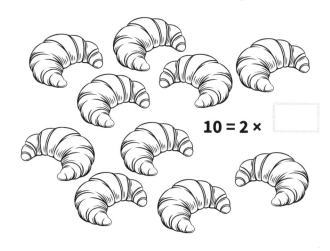

10 = 2 ×

Two of your friends are arguing over a pile of 22 football cards, saying they each want half of them. How many should each of them get?

22 = 2 ×

5

THE 5 TIMES TABLE

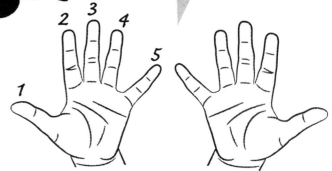

5 × 2 = 10

The awesome thing about the 5 times table is that you have a ready-made calculator (your fingers) to help you out!

Handy, eh? 🙂

TIMES TABLE TIME!

5 × 5 =

5 × 12 =

5 × 1 =

5 × 6 =

5 × 11 =

5 × 8 =

5 × 7 =

5 × 10 =

5 × 3 =

5 × 2 =

5 × 4 =

5 × 9 =

Why don't you and a friend test each other out on these problems?

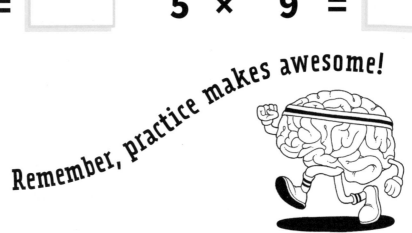

Remember, practice makes awesome!

10 50 55 61
35 27 42

MIND-BLOWING MULTIPLES

Circle all of the numbers above that **aren't** multiples of 5.

POCKET MONEY

Just kidding, it's not real money, but can you work out the value of the coins in each pile?

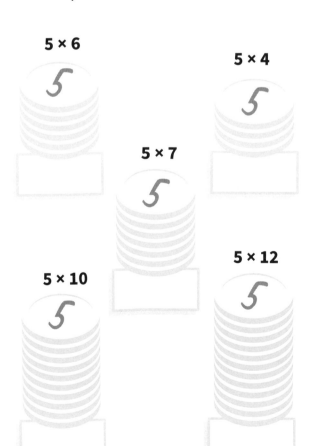

5 × 6

5 × 4

5 × 7

5 × 10

5 × 12

JUST A MINUTE

The minutes on a clock face are divided into groups of 5, with each number on the clock representing 5 minutes.

How many minutes are past the hour when the minute hand is pointing to the 6?

_____ **minutes**

How many minutes are past the hour when the minute hand is pointing to the 11?

_____ **minutes**

How many minutes are past the hour when the minute hand is pointing to the 4?

_____ **minutes**

How many minutes are past the hour when the minute hand is pointing to the 7?

_____ **minutes**

Complete these clock faces by drawing in the minute hand so that it points to the right number.

20 minutes

15 minutes

50 minutes

40 minutes

THE 10 TIMES TABLE

$10 \times 3 = 30$

$3 \longrightarrow 30$

I love the number 10, because when you multiply by 10, the digits move one place to the left, leaving a gap which you fill with a zero. Brilliant! So, be positive, stay focused – and let's get going!

TIMES TABLE TIME!

$10 \times 8 =$ ___

$10 \times 6 =$ ___

$10 \times 10 =$ ___

$10 \times 4 =$ ___

$10 \times 1 =$ ___

$10 \times 7 =$ ___

$10 \times 3 =$ ___

$10 \times 9 =$ ___

$10 \times 12 =$ ___

$10 \times 11 =$ ___

$10 \times 5 =$ ___

$10 \times 2 =$ ___

I bet you did these quite quickly, didn't you?

Fantastic work.

Times tables tips

Multiplying any number by 10, even a number with decimals, moves all of the digits one place to the left. Units become tens, tens become hundreds, hundreds become thousands, and so on.

THE POWER OF TENS!

Each group has 10 of each item. Calculate how many there are in total.

How many pongy trainers?

How many tortoises?

How many bicycles?

How many ping pong balls?

How many apples?

ALL CHANGE!

If you had £1 (100p), how many 10p coins would you get in your change if you bought the following:

Chocolate bar – 60p ⬚

Apple – 30p ⬚

Tennis ball – 70p ⬚

Toy car – 90p ⬚

10 *10* *10*

MIND-BLOWING MULTIPLES

*Circle all of the numbers below that **aren't** multiples of 10.*

50   62   86   92   100   60   10

FINGERS AND TOES

You can use your toes as well as your fingers to help you count in tens. Make sure your feet are clean first …

Each person has 10 fingers (including thumbs) and 10 toes.

How many fingers are there in a group of 6 people? ⬚

How many toes are there in a group of 11 people? ⬚

How many fingers are there in a group of 3 people? ⬚

How many toes are there in a group of 8 people? ⬚

THE 4 TIMES TABLE

16

12

0

8

4

Just like the 2 times table, every answer to the 4 times table is an even number.

Practise your 4 times table here and become Kid Awesome!

Times tables tips

One simple way to multiply by 4 is to double a number and then double it again.

TIMES TABLE TIME!

$4 \times 9 =$ ☐ $4 \times 7 =$ ☐

$4 \times 1 =$ ☐ $4 \times 8 =$ ☐

$4 \times 11 =$ ☐ $4 \times 2 =$ ☐

$4 \times 3 =$ ☐ $4 \times 4 =$ ☐

$4 \times 12 =$ ☐ $4 \times 10 =$ ☐

$4 \times 5 =$ ☐ $4 \times 6 =$ ☐

GROUPS OF 4

Each camel has 4 legs. How many legs are there on 4 camels?

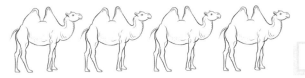

[ ] **legs**

Each taxi cab has 4 wheels. How many wheels are there on 7 taxi cabs?

[ ] **wheels**

My house has 4 windows. How many windows are there on 12 similar houses?

[ ] **windows**

Each chair has 4 legs. How many legs are there on 8 chairs?

[ ] **legs**

MIND-BLOWING MULTIPLES

Circle all of the numbers on the right that **aren't** multiples of 4.

16   18   12   24   40   30   15

SHARE AND SHARE ALIKE

Draw lines to divide up these items so that you and your three friends each have the same amount.

24 apples

48 biscuits

16 ping pong balls

12 croissants

11

THE 11 TIMES TABLE

Well done! We're on to the 11s now and you are making awesome progress through your times tables. Keep going!

TIMES TABLE TIME!

11 × 4 =

11 × 7 =

11 × 1 =

11 × 9 =

11 × 12 =

11 × 10 =

11 × 3 =

11 × 11 =

11 × 6 =

11 × 2 =

11 × 5 =

11 × 8 =

How did you do with your 11 times table? If you got a few wrong, why not try again? You'll get more right next time.

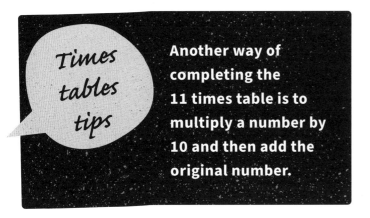

Another way of completing the 11 times table is to multiply a number by 10 and then add the original number.

WORDY PROBLEMS

Work out these problems. It might help to say them out loud at first.

MIND-BLOWING MULTIPLES

Circle all of the numbers below that **aren't** multiples of 11.

22 55 *76* 133 99 25 110

TEAM WORK

There are 11 players in a girls' school football team. Work out how many players there are in:

5 different teams ☐ **players**

12 different teams ☐ **players**

8 different teams ☐ **players**

10 different teams ☐ **players**

6 different teams ☐ **players**

Eleven times three equals ☐

Eleven times seven equals ☐

Eleven times eleven equals ☐

Eleven times two equals ☐

Eleven times nine equals ☐

THE 3 TIMES TABLE

For example

$$3 \times 5 = 15$$

$$1 + 5 = 6$$

One trick to learning your 3 times table is that the digits in your answer should add together to form 3, 6 or 9. (Oh wait! The 369 was also the bus I used to get to table tennis training ...)

TIMES TABLE TIME!

$3 \times 12 =$ ⬜ $3 \times 11 =$ ⬜

$3 \times 4 =$ ⬜ $3 \times 6 =$ ⬜

$3 \times 8 =$ ⬜ $3 \times 7 =$ ⬜

$3 \times 1 =$ ⬜ $3 \times 9 =$ ⬜

$3 \times 5 =$ ⬜ $3 \times 10 =$ ⬜

$3 \times 2 =$ ⬜ $3 \times 3 =$ ⬜

Don't stop now! You'll smash the 3s!

Times tables tips

The sum of the digits in any multiple of 3 will form a multiple of 3 when added together, even for bigger numbers. So 156: 1 + 5 + 6 = 12

THE POWER OF 3!

How many lights are there on 5 sets of traffic lights?

[ ] **lights**

How many sides are there on 7 triangles?

[ ] **sides**

How many leaves are there on 10 stalks of clover?

[ ] **leaves**

MIND-BLOWING MULTIPLES

Circle all of the numbers below that **aren't** multiples of 3.

33   6   9   7   26   18   13

WORDY PROBLEMS

Work out these problems. Remember, it might help to read them out loud first.

Three times five equals

[ ]

Three times seven equals

[ ]

Three times eight equals

[ ]

Three times twelve equals

[ ]

Three times nine equals

[ ]

THE 6 TIMES TABLE

6   48
12   18
24   36
30   60   42

Learning times tables is easier if you can see patterns in the answers. Write out the answers to the 6 times table in order and see if you can see a pattern!

TIMES TABLE TIME!

6 × 1 =   6 × 7 =

6 × 6 =   6 × 5 =

6 × 12 =   6 × 2 =

6 × 3 =   6 × 4 =

6 × 8 =   6 × 9 =

6 × 10 =   6 × 11 =

Get good at 6s by challenging yourself. If you practise hard it will get easier each time!

BOILED, POACHED, FRIED OR SCRAMBLED?

Eggs usually come in boxes of 6. So how many eggs are there in:

3 boxes?

|_____| **eggs**

6 boxes?

|_____| **eggs**

8 boxes?

|_____| **eggs**

12 boxes?

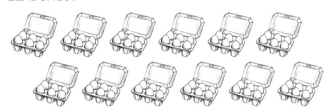

|_____| **eggs**

SLOWLY DOES IT!

There are 6 tortoises in a starting lane for a race. How many tortoises in:

5 starting lanes? |_____| **tortoises**

2 starting lanes? |_____| **tortoises**

4 starting lanes? |_____| **tortoises**

3 starting lanes? |_____| **tortoises**

MIND-BLOWING MULTIPLES

42   25   18   6   74   16   36

Circle all of the numbers above that **aren't** *multiples of 6.*

MATHS MATCH

Match each calculation to its correct answer. Draw a line linking the calculation with its answer.

6 × 6 =	72
6 × 10 =	36
6 × 4 =	24
6 × 12 =	66
6 × 11 =	60

THE 9 TIMES TABLE

For example:

9×1

$= 10 \times 1 - 1$

Awesome work so far! One simple way to learn your 9 times table is to multiply a number by 10 and then subtract the original number.

TIMES TABLE TIME!

$9 \times 6 =$ 　　　　$9 \times 7 =$

$9 \times 9 =$ 　　　　$9 \times 1 =$

$9 \times 5 =$ 　　　　$9 \times 8 =$

$9 \times 12 =$ 　　　　$9 \times 10 =$

$9 \times 2 =$ 　　　　$9 \times 4 =$

$9 \times 3 =$ 　　　　$9 \times 11 =$

9s can be tricky, but really STRETCH yourself – and soon you'll be saying your 9s in your sleep! Zzzzzzzz

Times tables tips

If you add together the digits for the answers up to 9 times 10, they all come to 9.

So: 9 × 5 = 45

4 + 5 = 9

MIND-BLOWING MULTIPLES

Circle all of the numbers below that **aren't** multiples of 9.

18   64   36   26

9   46   81

MATHS MATCH

Match these calculations with the correct answers. Draw a line linking the calculation with its answer.

9 × 7 =   54

9 × 11 =   63

9 × 4 =   108

9 × 6 =   99

9 × 12 =   36

WORDY PROBLEMS

Work out these word problems. Remember, it might help to read them out loud at first.

Nine times five equals

Nine multiplied by nine equals

Nine times ten equals

Nine times two equals

Nine multiplied by seven equals

THE 7 TIMES TABLE

The number 7 is my lucky number, but 7s can be tricky to learn. So let's get practising!

TIMES TABLE TIME!

$7 \times 7 =$ ⬜ $7 \times 2 =$ ⬜

$7 \times 12 =$ ⬜ $7 \times 9 =$ ⬜

$7 \times 3 =$ ⬜ $7 \times 10 =$ ⬜

$7 \times 4 =$ ⬜ $7 \times 1 =$ ⬜

$7 \times 5 =$ ⬜ $7 \times 11 =$ ⬜

$7 \times 6 =$ ⬜ $7 \times 8 =$ ⬜

Don't worry about making mistakes. They help you learn!

MIND-BLOWING MULTIPLES

*Circle all of the numbers that **aren't** multiples of 7.*

14   22

49   34   7   83   42

7 DAYS

There are 7 days in a week. How many days are there in:

7 weeks   =   ☐ days

10 weeks   =   ☐ days

4 weeks   =   ☐ days

8 weeks   =   ☐ days

12 weeks   =   ☐ days

Times tables tips

Here is my tried-and-tested method of learning the 7 times table.

Write out this grid:	0	1	2
	2	3	4
	4	5	6

Then write out this grid:	7	4	1
	8	5	2
	9	6	3

Now combine the two grids to make the answers to the 7 times table:	07	14	21
	28	35	42
	49	56	63

WORDY PROBLEMS

Work out these word problems. Remember, it might help to read them out loud at first.

Seven times six equals

Seven times eleven equals

☐

Seven multiplied by three equals

☐

Seven multiplied by nine equals

☐

Seven times two equals

☐

☐

8 TIMES TABLE

8 × 3

=

3 × 8

Remember that every problem in a times table has a twin! For example, 8 x 3 will give you the same answer as 3 x 8. (The answer is 24 both times!)

TIMES TABLE TIME!

8 × 3 =

8 × 12 =

8 × 7 =

8 × 9 =

8 × 1 =

8 × 10 =

8 × 8 =

8 × 4 =

8 × 2 =

8 × 11 =

8 × 6 =

8 × 5 =

It's great to get feedback on your tables.
It will help you get better!

Times tables tips

If you know your 4 times table, then you can work out the 8 times table by simply doubling each answer. For example: 8 × 3 = 24, which is twice 4 × 3 = 12.

MIND-BLOWING MULTIPLES

Circle all of the numbers below that **aren't** multiples of 8.

32   45   62   24   56   96   18

MATHS MATCH

Match these calculations with the correct answers. Draw a line linking the calculation with its answer.

8 × 8 =   16

8 × 2 =   64

8 × 9 =   32

8 × 11 =   88

8 × 4 =   72

IT'S A BUG'S LIFE

A spider has 8 legs (shudder). How many legs are there on:

8 spiders

[ ] **legs**

5 spiders

[ ] **legs**

3 spiders

[ ] **legs**

10 spiders

[ ] **legs**

Now forget about spiders and get on with your day!

23

THE 12 TIMES TABLE

3×12
2×12 11×12
5×12
4×12
8×12
9×12 7×12
10×12 6×12

Fantastic work! 12s is the last times table table you need to learn and you've already come across most of the calculations. You only need to learn 12 × 12!

12×12

TIMES TABLE TIME!

$12 \times 5 =$ ☐ $12 \times 6 =$ ☐

$12 \times 12 =$ ☐ $12 \times 1 =$ ☐

$12 \times 2 =$ ☐ $12 \times 8 =$ ☐

$12 \times 11 =$ ☐ $12 \times 10 =$ ☐

$12 \times 4 =$ ☐ $12 \times 9 =$ ☐

$12 \times 3 =$ ☐ $12 \times 7 =$ ☐

Did you get them all right? If not, don't give up! Getting them wrong will help you get them right next time!

Times tables tips

Another name for 12 is a dozen, and a dozen dozen (12 × 12 or 144) is called a gross.

MATHS MATCH

Match these problems by drawing a line to the correct answer.

12 × 8 =   60

12 × 5 =   144

12 × 12 =   96

12 × 3 =   108

12 × 9 =   36

MIND-BLOWING MULTIPLES

Circle all of the numbers below that **aren't** multiples of 12.

48   26   60   94

23   72   108

WORDY PROBLEMS

Work out these word problems. Remember, it might help to read them out loud at first.

Twelve times eight equals

Twelve times six equals

Twelve times ten equals

Twelve times four equals

Twelve times five equals

"TAKE A RISK, DARE TO FAIL" TEST

> Now see how amazing you are and test your times tables knowledge!

THE 2 TIMES TABLE

2 × 12 = [ ]

2 × 4 = [ ]

Circle all of the numbers to the right that **aren't** multiples of 2.

12　　5　16　13
4　　10　11

How many are there in 8 pairs?

[ ]

THE 5 TIMES TABLE

5 × 6 = [ ]

5 × 9 = [ ]

How many minutes are past the hour when the minute hand is pointing to the 10?

[ ] minutes

Draw in the minute hand on this clock face so that it points to 35 minutes past the hour.

THE 10 TIMES TABLE

10 × 4 = [ ]

10 × 10 = [ ]

How many fingers are there in a group of 7 people?

[ ] fingers

How many ping pong balls?

[ ]

THE 4 TIMES TABLE

4 × 11 = [ ]

4 × 12 = [ ]

Each taxi has 4 wheels. How many wheels are there on 4 taxis?

[ ] wheels

Circle all of the numbers that **aren't** multiples of 4.

16　24
12　40
22　10　7

THE 11 TIMES TABLE

11 × 4 = [ ]

11 × 11 = [ ]

There are 11 players in a girls' school football team. How many players are there in:

3 different teams [ ]

7 different teams [ ]

12 different teams [ ]

> Eleven times eight equals

[ ]

THE 3 TIMES TABLE

Circle all of the numbers below that **aren't** multiples of 3.

33   5   9   15
    12   28   14

$3 \times 12 =$ ⬚

How many sides are there on 6 triangles?

$3 \times 5 =$ ⬚

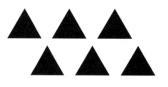

⬚ **sides**

THE 6 TIMES TABLE

Eggs usually come in boxes of 6. So how many eggs are there in 7 boxes?

⬚ **eggs**

$6 \times 12 =$ ⬚

A tortoise race has 6 tortoises taking part. How many tortoises would take part in 6 races?

$6 \times 9 =$ ⬚

⬚ **tortoises**

THE 9 TIMES TABLE

Match the problems by drawing a line to the correct answer!

$9 \times 9 =$ ⬚

$9 \times 5 =$ 99
$9 \times 11 =$ 45
$9 \times 3 =$ 90
$9 \times 10 =$ 27

$9 \times 4 =$ ⬚

Circle all of the numbers below that **aren't** multiples of 9.

18   61   36   28
    45   44   108

THE 7 TIMES TABLE

There are 7 days in a week. How many days are there in:

3 weeks   =   days

6 weeks   =   days

$7 \times 7 =$ ⬚

$7 \times 9 =$ ⬚

seven multiplied by five equals

THE 8 TIMES TABLE

Circle all of the numbers on the right that **aren't** multiples of 8.

$8 \times 3 =$ ⬚

32   61
    47   48
96
    24   20

A spider has 8 legs (shudder). How many legs are there in total on 7 spiders?

$8 \times 12 =$ ⬚

⬚ **legs**

THE 12 TIMES TABLE

Match the problems by drawing a line to the correct answer!

$12 \times 5 =$ ⬚

$12 \times 7 =$ 48
$12 \times 4 =$ 144
$12 \times 12 =$ 84
$12 \times 3 =$ 36

$12 \times 11 =$ ⬚

Twelve times seven equals

ANSWERS

Check your answers here. Don't worry if some of them are wrong. You'll get there in the end because ... You Are Awesome!

Pages 4–5

TIMES TABLE TIME!

2 × 3 = 6
2 × 6 = 12
2 × 9 = 18
2 × 1 = 2
2 × 4 = 8
2 × 8 = 16
2 × 2 = 4
2 × 10 = 20
2 × 12 = 24
2 × 5 = 10
2 × 11 = 22

PAIRS

3

12

10

MIND-BLOWING MULTIPLES

4 8 ⑦ 12 10 ⑨ ⑰ 18

HALVES

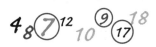
12 = 2 × 6

10 = 2 × 5

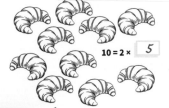

22 = 2 × 11

Pages 6–7

TIMES TABLE TIME!

5 × 5 = 25
5 × 1 = 5
5 × 11 = 55
5 × 7 = 35
5 × 3 = 15
5 × 4 = 20
5 × 12 = 60
5 × 6 = 30
5 × 8 = 40
5 × 10 = 50
5 × 2 = 10
5 × 9 = 45

JUST A MINUTE

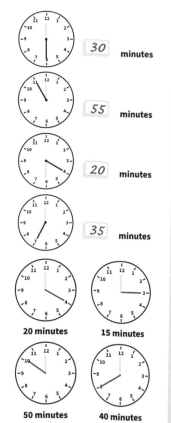

30 minutes

55 minutes

20 minutes

35 minutes

20 minutes   15 minutes

50 minutes   40 minutes

MIND-BLOWING MULTIPLES

10   50   55
35   ㉗   ㊷   ⑥①

POCKET MONEY

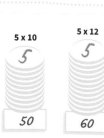

5 x 6	5 x 7	5 x 4	5 x 10	5 x 12
5	5	5	5	5
30	35	20	50	60

28

Pages 8–9

TIMES TABLE TIME!

10 × 8 = *80*

10 × 10 = *100*

10 × 1 = *10*

10 × 3 = *30*

10 × 12 = *120*

10 × 5 = *50*

10 × 6 = *60*

10 × 4 = *40*

10 × 7 = *70*

10 × 9 = *90*

10 × 11 = *110*

10 × 2 = *20*

THE POWER OF TENS

30

50

20

80

70

ALL CHANGE!

Chocolate bar – 60p   *4*

Apple – 30p   *7*

Tennis ball – 70p   *3*

Toy car – 90p   *1*

FINGERS AND TOES

How many fingers are there in a group of 6 people?   *60*

How many toes are there in a group of 11 people?   *110*

How many fingers are there in a group of 3 people?   *30*

How many toes are there in a group of 8 people?   *80*

MIND-BLOWING MULTIPLES

50 42 **86** 92 60 100 10

Pages 10–11

TIMES TABLE TIME!

4 × 9 = *36*

4 × 1 = *4*

4 × 11 = *44*

4 × 3 = *12*

4 × 12 = *48*

4 × 5 = *20*

4 × 7 = *28*

4 × 8 = *32*

4 × 2 = *8*

4 × 4 = *16*

4 × 10 = *40*

4 × 6 = *24*

GROUPS OF 4

16 legs

28 wheels

48 windows

32 legs

MIND-BLOWING MULTIPLES

16 18 12 24 40 30 15

SHARE AND SHARE ALIKE

Pages 12–13

TIMES TABLE TIME!

11 × 4 = *44*   11 × 7 = *77*

11 × 1 = *11*   11 × 9 = *99*

11 × 12 = *132*   11 × 10 = *110*

11 × 3 = *33*   11 × 11 = *121*

11 × 6 = *66*   11 × 2 = *22*

11 × 5 = *55*   11 × 8 = *88*

TEAM WORK

5 different teams   *55* players   10 different teams   *110* players

12 different teams   *132* players   6 different teams   *66* players

8 different teams   *88* players

MIND-BLOWING MULTIPLES

22 76 133 99 55 110 25

WORDY PROBLEMS

Eleven times three equals   *33*

Eleven times seven equals   *77*

Eleven times eleven equals   *121*

Eleven times two equals   *22*

Eleven times nine equals   *99*

Pages 14–15

TIMES TABLE TIME!

3 × 12 = 36   3 × 11 = 33

3 × 4 = 12   3 × 6 = 18

3 × 8 = 24   3 × 7 = 21

3 × 1 = 3   3 × 9 = 27

3 × 5 = 15   3 × 10 = 30

3 × 2 = 6   3 × 3 = 9

MIND-BLOWING MULTIPLES

33   6   9   7   26   18   13

WORDY PROBLEMS

Three times five equals 15

Three times seven equals 21

Three times eight equals 24

Three times twelve equals 36

Three times nine equals 27

THE POWER OF 3

15 lights

21 sides

30 leaves

Pages 16–17

TIMES TABLE TIME!

6 × 1 = 6   6 × 7 = 42

6 × 6 = 36   6 × 5 = 30

6 × 12 = 72   6 × 2 = 12

6 × 3 = 18   6 × 4 = 24

6 × 8 = 48   6 × 9 = 54

6 × 10 = 60   6 × 11 = 66

BOILED, POACHED, FRIED OR SCRAMBLED?

3 boxes? — 18 eggs

6 boxes? — 36 eggs

8 boxes? — 48 eggs

12 boxes? — 72 eggs

MIND-BLOWING MULTIPLES

42   25   18   6   74   16   36

MATHS MATCH

6 × 6 = 72
6 × 10 = 36
6 × 4 = 24
6 × 12 = 66
6 × 11 = 60

SLOWLY DOES IT!

5 starting lanes? — 30 tortoises

2 starting lanes? — 12 tortoises

4 starting lanes? — 24 tortoises

3 starting lanes? — 18 tortoises

Pages 18–19

TIMES TABLE TIME!

9 × 6 = 54

9 × 9 = 81

9 × 5 = 45

9 × 12 = 108

9 × 2 = 18

9 × 3 = 27

9 × 7 = 63

9 × 1 = 9

9 × 8 = 72

9 × 10 = 90

9 × 4 = 36

9 × 11 = 99

WORDY PROBLEMS

Nine times five equals 45

Nine multiplied by nine equals 81

Nine times ten equals 90

Nine times two equals 18

Nine multiplied by seven equals 63

MATHS MATCH

9 × 7 = 54
9 × 11 = 63
9 × 4 = 108
9 × 6 = 99
9 × 12 = 36

MIND-BLOWING MULTIPLES

18   64   36   26   9   46   81

Pages 20–21

TIMES TABLE TIME!

7 × 7 = 49   7 × 2 = 14

7 × 12 = 84   7 × 9 = 63

7 × 3 = 21   7 × 10 = 70

7 × 4 = 28   7 × 1 = 7

7 × 5 = 35   7 × 11 = 77

7 × 6 = 42   7 × 8 = 56

MIND-BLOWING MULTIPLES

34   14   22

49   7   83   42

7 DAYS

7 weeks	=	49 days
10 weeks	=	70 days
4 weeks	=	28 days
8 weeks	=	56 days
12 weeks	=	84 days

WORDY PROBLEMS

Seven times six equals

42

Seven times eleven equals

77

Seven multiplied by three equals

21

Seven multiplied by nine equals

63

Seven times two equals

14

Pages 22–23

TIMES TABLE TIME!

8 × 3 = 24

8 × 7 = 56

8 × 1 = 8

8 × 8 = 64

8 × 2 = 16

8 × 6 = 48

8 × 12 = 96

8 × 9 = 72

8 × 10 = 80

8 × 4 = 32

8 × 11 = 88

8 × 5 = 40

MIND-BLOWING MULTIPLES

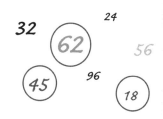

32   24

62   56

45   96   18

IT'S A BUG'S LIFE

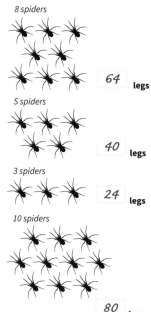

8 spiders

64 legs

5 spiders

40 legs

3 spiders

24 legs

10 spiders

80 legs

MATHS MATCH

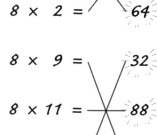

8 × 8 =   16

8 × 2 =   64

8 × 9 =   32

8 × 11 =   88

8 × 4 =   72

Pages 24–25

TIMES TABLE TIME!

12 × 5 = 60   12 × 4 = 48   12 × 8 = 96

12 × 12 = 144   12 × 3 = 36   12 × 10 = 120

12 × 2 = 24   12 × 6 = 72   12 × 9 = 108

12 × 11 = 22   12 × 1 = 12   12 × 7 = 84

MIND-BLOWING MULTIPLES

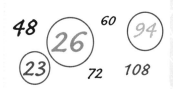

48   26   60   94

23   72   108

MATHS MATCH

12 × 8 =   60

12 × 5 =   144

12 × 12 =   96

12 × 3 =   108

12 × 9 =   36

WORDY PROBLEMS

Twelve times eight equals

96

Twelve times six equals

72

Twelve times ten equals

120

Twelve times four equals

48

Twelve times five equals

60

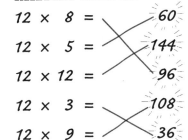

THE 2 TIMES TABLE

$2 \times 12 =$ 24 $2 \times 4 =$ 8

12   ⑤   *16*   ⑬

4   *10*   ⑪

How many are there in 8 pairs?

16

THE 5 TIMES TABLE

$5 \times 6 =$ 30 $5 \times 9 =$ 45

   50

minutes

THE 10 TIMES TABLE

$10 \times 4 =$ 40 $10 \times 10 =$ 100

70

fingers

○○○○○ ○○○○○ ○○○○○
○○○○○ ○○○○○ ○○○○○

How many ping pong balls?   60

THE 4 TIMES TABLE

$4 \times 11 =$ 44 $4 \times 12 =$ 48

   16

wheels

16   *24*
  12   *40*
㉒   *10*   ⑦

THE 11 TIMES TABLE

$11 \times 4 =$ 44 $11 \times 11 =$ 121

3 different teams   33

7 different teams   77

12 different teams   132

Eleven times eight equals

88

THE 3 TIMES TABLE

$3 \times 12 =$ 36 $3 \times 5 =$ 15

33   ⑤   *9*   *15*

12   ㉘   ⑭

18   sides

THE 6 TIMES TABLE

$6 \times 12 =$ 72 $6 \times 9 =$ 54

42
eggs

36
tortoises

THE 9 TIMES TABLE

$9 \times 9 =$ 81 $9 \times 4 =$ 36

$9 \times 5 =$ —— 99
$9 \times 11 =$ —— 45
$9 \times 3 =$ —— 90
$9 \times 10 =$ —— 27

18   ㊶   *36*   ㉘
   45   ㊹   *108*

THE 7 TIMES TABLE

$7 \times 7 =$ 49 $7 \times 9 =$ 63

3 weeks =   21   days

6 weeks =   42   days

Seven multiplied by five equals

35

THE 8 TIMES TABLE

$8 \times 3 =$ 24 $8 \times 12 =$ 96

32   ㊶
㊼   *48*
96   *24*   ⑳

56
legs

THE 12 TIMES TABLE

$12 \times 5 =$ 60 $12 \times 11 =$ 132

$12 \times 7 =$ —— 48
$12 \times 4 =$ —— 144
$12 \times 12 =$ —— 84
$12 \times 3 =$ —— 36

Twelve times seven equals

84